EGMONT

We bring stories to life

First published in Great Britain 2009
by Egmont UK Limited
239 Kensington High Street
London W8 6SA

Originally published in Indonesia in 2008 by Komik Warna.

Ben 10 and all related characters and elements
are trademarks of and © Cartoon Network.
(s09)

ISBN 978 1 4052 4805 1
1 3 5 7 9 10 8 6 4 2

Printed in Italy

CREATED BY

DUNCAN ROULEAU, JOE CASEY,
JOE KELLY AND STEVEN T. SEAGLE

BEN 10™

WILDMUTT

GHOSTFREAK

HEATBLAST

BEN TENNYSON

DIAMONDHEAD

VOLUME 4

PERMANENT RETIREMENT

WRITTEN BY
MARSHA F. GRIFFIN

IT IS A SUNNY AFTERNOON AND BEN, GWEN AND GRANDPA MAX HAVE PULLED INTO AN ICE CREAM PARLOUR.

ICE CREAM   ICE CREAM

SUDDENLY, A CAR PULLS UP BEHIND GRANDPA MAX.

VRROOOM!

A MAN GETS OUT OF THE CAR AND WATCHES GRANDPA MAX WITHDRAW MONEY FROM THE CASHPOINT.

OUT OF THE WAY, GRANDPA!

I'VE GOT A MAJOR WITHDRAWAL TO MAKE.

WHAT DO YOU HAVE THAT IS NON-FAT AND HAS LESS THAN 3% SUGAR?

NAPKINS. NOW, WHAT ABOUT YOU, KID?

I'LL HAVE A . . . WHAT'S THAT NOISE?

BEN NOTICES THE TWO MEN OUTSIDE.

GOTTA GO!

HE ACTIVATES THE OMNITRIX.

BEEP!

CLANK!

HIT IT!

COOL!

THE CROOK STEPS ON THE GAS.

WE'RE GOING TO BE RICH!

THE CHAIN WRAPS AROUND UPGRADE'S ARM.

CLINK!

THWACK!

IT'S TIME FOR REVENGE!

WITH A HARD TUG, UPGRADE THROWS THE MAN UP INTO THE AIR.

WOAH!

THIS IS GOING TO BE SO BORING WITH ALL THESE OLD FOLKS. THEIR IDEA OF EXCITEMENT IS PROBABLY WATCHING THE GRASS GROW.

AAARGH!

WHOOSH!

SUDDENLY, BEN LOOKS OUT OF THE WINDOW AND NOTICES AN OLD MAN LOSE HIS FOOTING ON A ROOF . . .

. . . THEN THE OLD MAN LEAPS THROUGH THE AIR AND LANDS SAFELY ON THE GROUND!

HMM.

WOAH! DID YOU *SEE THAT*?

HUH?

SEE WHAT?

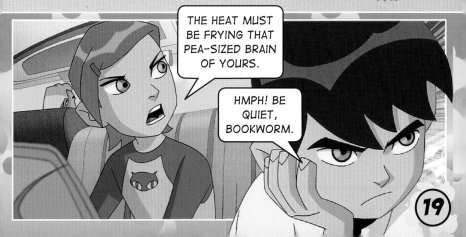

THE HEAT MUST BE FRYING THAT PEA-SIZED BRAIN OF YOURS.

HMPH! BE QUIET, BOOKWORM.

19

THEY FINALLY ARRIVE AT AUNT VERA'S HOUSE.

SERIOUSLY! WHY DO OLD PEOPLE HAVE TO LIVE IN PLACES THAT ARE SOOOO HOT?

HEY! WHAT'S THAT?

SPLASH!

HA HA . . . I GOTCHA!

HUH?

LOOKING AROUND, BEN NOTICES AUNT VERA'S NEIGHBOUR, MARTY.

. . . A CALL INDICATING ALARM OR EXCITEMENT!

MEANWHILE, BEN IS BUSY EATING AUNT VERA'S FOOD.

YUM!

I AM TOTALLY STUFFED.

HAVE YOU GOT ANY ROOM FOR SOME SWEETS?

NOW WE'RE TALKING!

MMMM!

UH! COFFEE? IN A SWEET? IS THIS SOME KIND OF A JOKE?

UH OH . . . LOOKS LIKE MY STOMACH ISN'T BEING FRIENDLY TODAY. I NEED TO USE THE BATHROOM!

BEN RUNS TOWARDS THE BATHROOM AT THE END OF THE HALL.

PHEW! FINALLY I GET SOME PEACE.

27

IT'S ATTACK OF THE OLD PEOPLE!

I HAVE TO GET OUT OF THIS PLACE!

BEN ACTIVATES THE OMNITRIX.

BEEP!

BEEP!

OH YEAH!

CHOOSING THE FORM OF *GHOSTFREAK*, BEN SLAMS DOWN THE FACE OF THE OMNITRIX.

IT'S TIME TO HAVE SOME FUN!

BEEP!

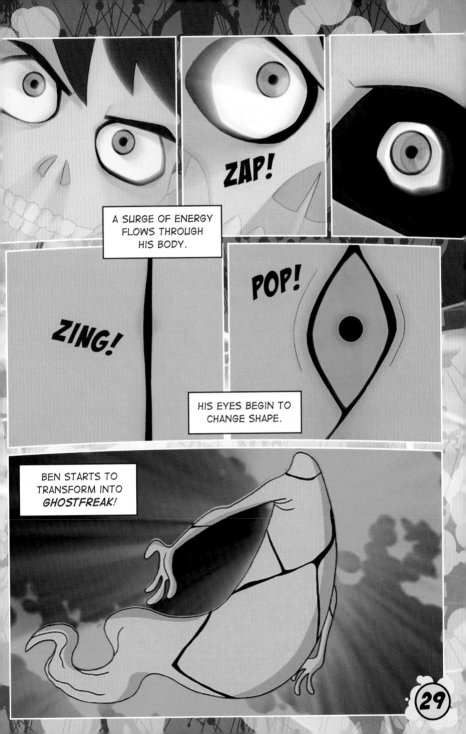

AS GHOSTFREAK, BEN BECOMES INVISIBLE AND FLIES THROUGH THE WALL.

. . . AND THIS ONE IS A VALENTINA.

MEANWHILE, GWEN IS STILL ENJOYING TALKING TO AUNT VERA.

YOU CAN HEAR THE SEA THROUGH IT.

LOSER!
LOOOOSER!

HAHAHA!

BEN?

UH . . . WHAT'S THAT SOUND?

SEE YOU LATER, GWEN!

GHOSTFREAK GLIDES THROUGH THE WALL AND FLIES OUT OF AUNT VERA'S HOUSE.

THERE HAS TO BE SOMETHING FUN TO DO AROUND HERE.

AT LAST! I'M OUT OF THAT HOUSE!

31

GHOSTFREAK SPOTS A GOLF CART PARKED IN FRONT OF A GARAGE.

OH, HELLO . . .

LOOK! I MUST BE GETTING OLD. THAT GOLF CART LOOKS LIKE IT'S DRIVING AROUND ON ITS OWN!

BUT GHOSTFREAK IS BEHIND THE WHEEL, DRIVING DOWN THE STREETS OF THE HOUSING COMPLEX!

VRROOM!

MMM . . . WHAT'S THAT SMELL?

SNIFF!
SNIFF!

APPLE PIE!

OOPS, SOMEBODY'S COMING.

GHOSTFREAK FOLLOWS THE DELICIOUS SMELL, WHICH LEADS HIM INTO A NEARBY HOUSE.

HE SEES AN OLD LADY TRYING TO SWAT A FLY.

STUPID FLY.

JUST YOU WAIT, I'M GOING TO SWALLOW YOU WHOLE!

GULP!

SWOOSH!

THE OLD LADY LEAPS UP ON TO THE CEILING, OPENS HER MOUTH TO CATCH THE FLY AND SWALLOWS IT!

33

THWACK!

YUCK! NO WAY! NINJA OLD PEOPLE!

GHOSTFREAK FINDS THE WHOLE EPISODE REALLY GROSS!

HUH? WHAT'S THAT NOISE?

SWOOSH!

THE WATER SPRINKLERS BURST INTO ACTION.

MEANWHILE, MARTY IS DRIVING ALONG THE ROAD IN HIS GOLF CART . . .

SWOOSH!

WOAH!

. . . WHEN HE SUDDENLY SEES WATER ON THE ROAD.

GRRR! I'M GONNA GET YOU, KID!

AAHHHH!

AWW!

BEN BREAKS FREE FROM MARTY'S STRONG GRIP.

AGHH!

THEN HE RUNS TOWARDS THE GATE TO FIND AN ESCAPE.

I'VE GOTTA GET OUT OF HERE!

THE GOLF CART LURCHES INTO ACTION AND BEN DRIVES AWAY AS FAST AS HE CAN.

BUT MARTY IS RUNNING AT SUPER SPEED AND IS CATCHING UP WITH THE CART!

VROOM!

RAAAA!

THEN MARTY STRETCHES OUT HIS ARMS . . .

BANG!

HUH?!

I'M GONNA GET YOU NOW!

. . . AND GRABS HOLD OF THE GOLF CART!

42

THE GOLF CART FLIPS UP INTO THE AIR . . .

. . . AND LANDS WITH A CRASH!

OWW, MY HEAD . . .

OH NO! HE'S STILL THERE!

SPLASH!

SUDDENLY, THE SPRINKLER BURSTS INTO ACTION AND SPRAYS WATER ALL OVER THE GARDEN.

THE WATER SPLASHES MARTY AND HE QUICKLY RUNS AWAY.

AAHH!

ARRGGHH!

SPLASH!

OH MAN! SOMEBODY TELL ME WHAT IS GOING ON HERE!

OVER AT MARTY'S HOUSE . . .

SSHH!

HELLO? ANYBODY HOME?

WELL, NOTHING HERE SEEMS OUT OF THE ORDINARY.

EXCEPT FOR WHAT HE ROLLED UP IN HIS RUG . . .

HE WAS HIDING SOMETHING IN HERE. I SWEAR!

50

LATER THAT EVENING, BACK AT AUNT VERA'S HOUSE . . .

NOW, YOU TWO GO TO SLEEP. I'LL BE IN THE GUEST ROOM IF YOU NEED ME.

BUT GRANDPA . . .

THERE'S NOTHING MORE WE CAN DO TONIGHT.

I'M GOING FOR AN EARLY WALK IN THE MORNING, BUT ONCE I'M BACK WE'LL CHECK THINGS OUT AGAIN. NOW GET SOME REST.

51

MEANWHILE IN AUNT VERA'S ROOM . . .

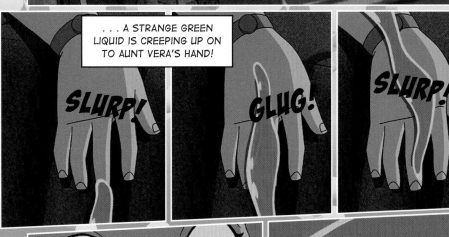

. . . A STRANGE GREEN LIQUID IS CREEPING UP ON TO AUNT VERA'S HAND!

SLURP!

GLUG!

SLURP!

GULP!

GLOOP!

THE SLIME SLIDES ON TO HER BED AND IT SOON COVERS HER WHOLE FACE!

BEN AND GWEN GO FOR A WALK AROUND THE COMPLEX TO SEE IF THEY CAN FIND OUT WHAT IS GOING ON.

SO, WHERE ARE WE HEADING, SHERLOCK?

WE NEED TO GET TO THAT TRAP DOOR BY THE DUMPSTER.

IT'S RIGHT OVER THERE.

JUST FOLLOW THE DISGUSTING SMELL.

WHY ARE THOSE OLD LADIES STARING AT US?

AAAHH!

AAAHH!

THWACK

FWOOSH!

BEN! WATCH OUT! DUCK!

RUN!

KA-BOOM!

WOAH!

AGHH!

WHOOSH!

OVER HERE!

GUYS, WHAT'S GOING ON?

THEY'RE EVERYWHERE!

I KNOW. COME OVER HERE. I'LL PROTECT YOU!

NO! THAT ISN'T GRANDPA MAX! WE HAVE TO GET OUT OF HERE!

AAHHH!

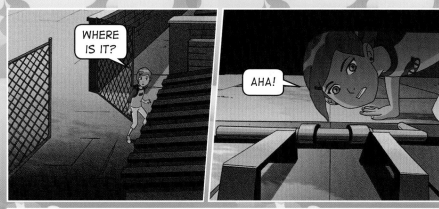

BEEP!

ZAP!

ZAP!

IN A FLASH, THE POWER OF THE OMNITRIX SURGES THROUGH BEN'S BODY.

A POWERFUL ORANGE LIGHT BEAMS OUT ACROSS THE SKY.

SWOOSH!

ZOOM!

THE OMNITRIX TRANSFORMS BEN INTO, *WILDMUTT*!

THWACK!

ROOAARRR!

WOAH! BEN! IT'S ME, GWEN!

CRASH!

WILDMUTT THROWS A HUGE REFUSE BIN AT THE POSSESSED PEOPLE.

FWOOSH!

THE BIN CRASHES ON TOP OF THEM, SMASHING THEM ALL INTO THE GROUND!

KA-BOOM!

AAHH!

GREEN LIQUID STARTS TO FLOW OUT FROM UNDERNEATH THE REFUSE BIN. THE OLD PEOPLE MORPH BACK INTO THEIR HUMAN FORMS.

GGRRR!

THAT WAS CLOSE!

GWEN PULLS OPEN THE HEAVY TRAPDOOR.

HANG ON! I'M COMING.

OKAY, LET'S GO!

HEY! BE CAREFUL!

WILDMUTT LEAPS THROUGH THE OPEN TRAP DOOR!

FWOOSH!

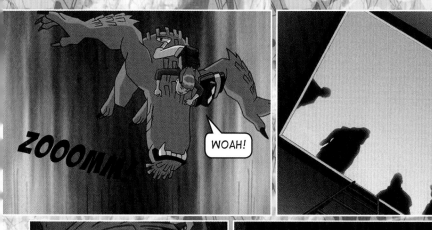

ZOOOMM!

WOAH!

UGH!

THUD!

THEY LAND WITH A CRASH AT THE BOTTOM OF THE PIT.

WHAT PART OF 'BE CAREFUL' DID YOU NOT UNDERSTAND?

THESE TUNNELS MUST GO UNDER THE WHOLE COMPLEX.

USING HIS SUPER SENSES, WILDMUTT DETECTS A STRANGE VIBRATION BEHIND HIM.

THWACK!

UH, WHOSE HANDS ARE THOSE?

AAGHH!

KA-THUD!

WILDMUTT BLOCKS THE ATTACK AND FLINGS THE POSSESSED GRANDPA MAX HIGH UP INTO THE AIR.

WILDMUTT AND GRANDPA MAX GET READY FOR BATTLE.

GRANDPA MAX SLAMS WILDMUTT INTO THE GROUND.

THEN GRANDPA MAX SWINGS A PUNCH AT WILDMUTT.

RAAAA!

BAM!

ARRGGHH!

WILDMUTT RETURNS THE ATTACK, BITING AND THROWING THE GRANDPA MAX IMPOSTER INTO THE ROCKS.

KA-BOOM!

THUD!

ROOAAARR!

AS WILDMUTT PREPARES TO LAUNCH HIS FINAL ATTACK, HE HEARS A FAMILIAR VOICE.

YOU WOULDN'T WANT TO HURT YOUR GRANDPA MAX, NOW WOULD YOU BEN?

SLAM!

GRRR?

MISLED BY WHAT THE CREATURE INSIDE GRANDPA MAX SAYS, WILDMUTT FALTERS. THE CREATURE SEIZES THE MOMENT AND LAUNCHES AN ATTACK.

FWOOSH!

HEY! SHORT, DUMB AND HAIRY! RULE NUMBER ONE – HE'S NOT GRANDPA! HE'S AN ALIEN FREAK!

AND THAT LEADS TO RULE NUMBER TWO – WE KICK ALIEN BUTT!

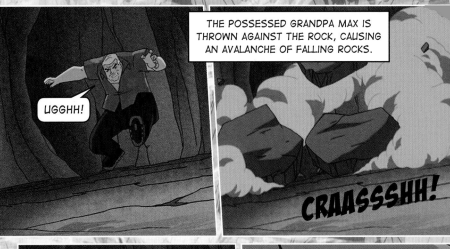

THE POSSESSED GRANDPA MAX IS THROWN AGAINST THE ROCK, CAUSING AN AVALANCHE OF FALLING ROCKS.

WILDMUTT CAN STILL SENSE A STRANGE VIBRATION.

UH!

HEY, FREAK SHOW, WHAT DO I LOOK LIKE, A CRASH TEST DUMMY?

LISTEN, I DON'T KNOW WHAT IT IS BUT I PICKED UP SOME KIND OF SCENT IN HERE.

COME AND LOOK DOWN HERE . . .

IT LOOKS LIKE ALL THE PEOPLE FROM THE RETIREMENT HOME HAVE BEEN TRAPPED INSIDE THOSE WEIRD GREEN EGGS!

YOU CAN FILL ME IN LATER.

ZAP!

THEN GWEN ACCIDENTALLY TOUCHES THE WALL BEHIND HER.

A YELLOW LIGHT BEAMS OUT ACROSS THE CAVE AND THE WALL SUDDENLY OPENS UP BEHIND HER . . .

WHAT IS THIS? WHERE AM I?

GWEN FINDS HERSELF IN ANOTHER STRANGE ROOM FILLED WITH THE EGGS THAT WERE HOLDING THE OLD PEOPLE CAPTIVE.

WHAT ARE ALL THESE EGGS DOING IN THIS WEIRD PLACE?

THEY'VE GOT AUNT VERA!

WE'VE GOT TO SAVE HER.

HMM.

BEN IMMEDIATELY ACTIVATES THE OMNITRIX.

BEEP!

YOU GUYS REALLY BURN ME UP.

BEEP!

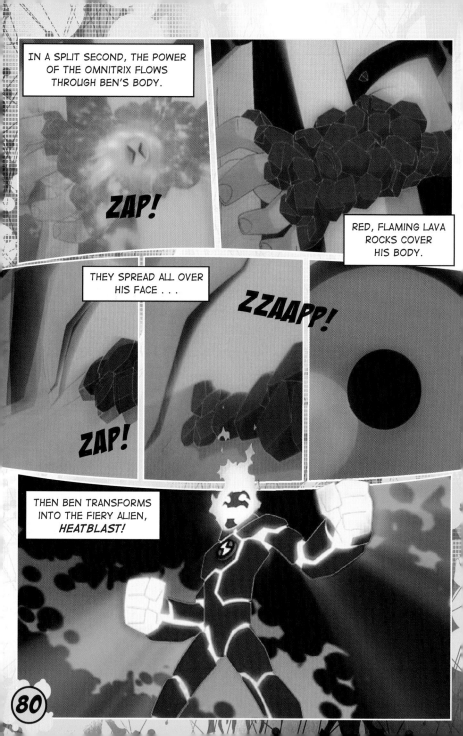

IN A SPLIT SECOND, THE POWER OF THE OMNITRIX FLOWS THROUGH BEN'S BODY.

ZAP!

RED, FLAMING LAVA ROCKS COVER HIS BODY.

THEY SPREAD ALL OVER HIS FACE . . .

ZZAAPP!

ZAP!

THEN BEN TRANSFORMS INTO THE FIERY ALIEN, *HEATBLAST!*

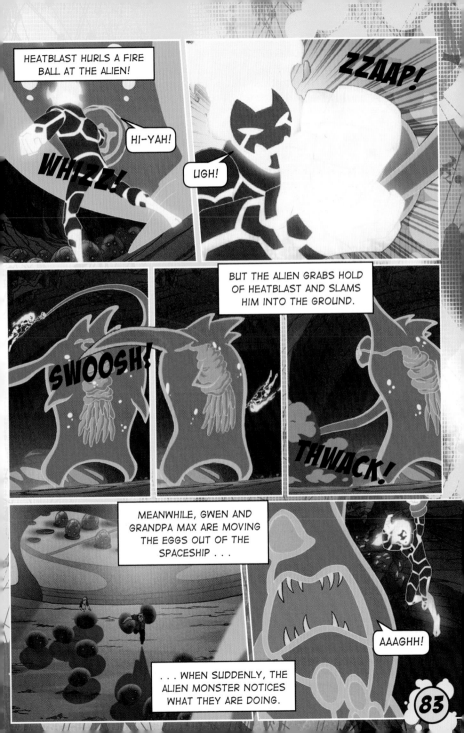

THE ALIEN THROWS SOME OF THE GREEN LIQUID FROM ITS BODY INTO THE AIR.

SLURP!

IT LANDS NEAR THE SHIP.

THE ALIEN CREATURE TAKES A SWIPE AT GWEN FROM BEHIND.

HER BACKPACK SNAPS AND GWEN CRASHES TO THE GROUND.

SNAP!

AAWW!

GWEN!

WATCH OUT!

AGH!

NOO!

THE ALIENS NOTICE A WATER PISTOL THAT HAS FALLEN FROM GWEN'S BAG.

THEY SLOWLY BACK AWAY FROM GWEN AND HER WATER PISTOL.

HEHE!

AGGHH!

THEY TURN AND RUN AS FAST AS THEY CAN!

TAKE THIS!

HEATBLAST SEES A WATER PIPE ABOVE HIM.

OH YEAH! THE SAME HAPPENED WHEN MARTY RAN FROM THE SPRINKLERS!

FWOOSH!

FWOOM!

HE SHOOTS A FIREBALL THROUGH THE ALIEN'S BODY.

IT HITS THE WATER PIPE DEAD ON!

BOOM!

THE PIPE BURSTS AND WATER GUSHES OUT OF IT!

AGH!

THE ALIEN DROPS HEATBLAST FROM ITS GRASP.

SEE YA LATER, SLIMEBALL!

AAAHH!

THE WATER COVERS THE ALIEN AND IT STARTS TO MELT!

GLUG!

LET'S GO!

SORRY, THERE'S NO DRIVE-THROUGH SERVICE HERE!

ACCEPTING DEFEAT, THE GREEN SLIMY ALIEN SLIDES BACK INTO ITS SPACESHIP.

WE MANAGED TO GET ALL OF THE EGGS OUT!

GLOOP!

GLUG!

SUDDENLY, THE SPACESHIP STARTS TO CHANGE COLOUR.

ZING!

ZAP!

IT SLOWLY LIFTS UP OFF THE GROUND.

ZOOM!

FWOOSH!

89

WOW!

THEN THE SPACESHIP ROCKETS UP INTO SPACE!

ZOOM!

WE SHOULD PUT THE OLD FOLK BACK IN THEIR HOUSES SO THEY THINK THEY NEVER LEFT.

THAT COULD TAKE HOURS.

GIVE ME A FEW MINUTES. I'LL SEE IF *XLR8* CAN HELP OUT!

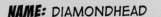

NAME: DIAMONDHEAD

ALIEN BACKGROUND:
DESCENDS FROM THE
PLANET PETROPIA.
PETROPIA IS LAYERED
WITH CRYSTALS

PHYSICAL FACT:
DIAMONHEAD IS
MADE UP OF DENSE
CRYSTALS. HE CAN
GROW BACK BODY
PARTS THAT HAVE BEEN
LOST IN BATTLE

SUPER POWER: DIAMONDHEAD IS
ALMOST INVINCIBLE. HE CAN CREATE
THORN–LIKE WEAPONS FROM HIS
OWN BODY AND CAN USE THEM TO CUT
THROUGH ANYTHING IN A SPLIT SECOND!

INTERESTING FACT: HIS BODY CAN FUNCTION AS A PRISM
TO RELFECT LASER ATTACKS BACK AT THE ENEMY!

WEAKNESS: DIAMONDHEAD'S CRYSTAL WEAPONS CAN
SHATTER WHEN SLAMMED AGAINST SOLID OBJECTS

DIAMONDHEAD

EVER WISHED THE SCHOOL HOLIDAYS COULD BE MORE INTERESTING?

WIN A £20 EGMONT BOOK VOUCHER EVERY MONTH!

WIN!

Simply go to
WWW.EGMONT.CO.UK/COMPETITION
and tell us which adventures
you would like to go on!